Edition Schott

Sophia Giustani Dussek

1775 – 1847

Sonata

for Harp
für Harfe

C minor / c-Moll / Ut mineur
opus 2

Edited by / Herausgegeben von
Nicanor Zabaleta

BSS 38511
ISMN 979-0-001-10976-5

www.schott-music.com

Mainz · London · Berlin · Madrid · New York · Paris · Prague · Tokyo · Toronto
© 1954 SCHOTT MUSIC Ltd, London · © renewed 1982 assigned to SCHOTT MUSIC GmbH & Co. KG, Mainz · Printed in Germany

Sonata

S. G. Dussek
1775 – 1847

4

6

Andantino

Rondo Allegro

Minore

Majore

Sophia Giustani Dussek wurde am 1. Mai 1775 in Edinburgh/Schottland als Tochter des aus Italien stammenden Komponisten und Verlegers Domenico Corri geboren. 1792 heiratete sie Johann Ludwig Dussek. Bekannt wurde Sophia als Sopranistin, Harfenistin, Pianistin und Komponistin. Sie komponierte ausschließlich kammermusikalische Werke, meist Solosonaten für Harfe oder Klavier sowie einige Airs mit Variationen für Harfe. Sophia Giustani Dussek starb 1847 in London.

Ihr Opus 2 umfasst zwei Bände von jeweils drei Sonaten für Harfe. Die vorliegende Sonate in c-Moll stammt aus dem ersten Band, der 1796 bei Pleyel in Paris erschien. Da der Vorname des Komponisten in der Ausgabe nicht genannt wurde, schrieb man diese drei Sonaten fälschlicherweise dem damals in Paris recht bekannten Johann Ludwig Dussek zu (vgl. RISM, D 4605). In dessen von Howard Craw erstellten Werkverzeichnis wird jedoch ein Band mit vier Violinsonaten als Opus 2 bezeichnet. Eine bei Corri, Dussek & Co. in London und Edinburgh erschienene Ausgabe dieser Harfensonaten wird Sophia Dussek zugeschrieben (vgl. RISM, D 4649).

Die Neuauflage der Sonate bei Schott Musik International wurde entsprechend korrigiert.

Sophia Giustani Dussek was born at May 1, 1775 in Edinburgh/Scotland as a daughter of the Italian composer and music publisher Domenico Corri. In 1792, she married Johann Ludwig Dussek. She became well known as a soprano, harpist, pianist and composer. Her compositions are exclusively works for chamber music, mainly solo sonatas for the harp or the piano and some airs with variations for the harp. Sophia Giustani Dussek died in London in 1847.

Her opus 2 consists of two books of three sonatas each for the harp. The sonata in c-minor appears in the first book, published by Pleyel in Paris in 1796. In this edition, the composer's first name was not mentioned, so the sonatas were falsely ascribed to Johann Ludwig Dussek, who was quite well known in Paris at this time (cf. RISM, D 4605). In the "Thematic index of the works of J.L. Dussek" by Howard Craw opus 2 is given as a set of 4 violin sonatas. An edition of the harp sonatas published by Corri, Dussek & Co. in London and Edinburgh is ascribed to Sophia Dussek (cf. RISM, D 4649).

The new edition of the sonata published by Schott Music International has been corrected according to this failure.